Dupe 'em
and
Dope 'em

Robert Clyde Affolter

Innate Foundation Publishing

Innate Foundation Publishing
Bellingham, WA USA

www.InnateFoundation.com

Printed in USA

Preface

Has there been a conspiracy between the government, pharmaceutical industry and the insurance industry to trick or dupe us into taking more of their drugs or dope? This book is a combination of two books I wrote in 2009 and published as ebooks. Some prefer to hold a book in their hands and take it with them. This is for them.

In 2009, the health care debate was going full steam. As of this writing, Americans now have national health care legislation. However, the debate will continue. What conditions should be covered? What treatments should be approved? How will we control costs?

For over a century, we have tried to make sense of our lives using an evolution-based construct. Perhaps we have gone as far as that model can take us. Perhaps it is time to approach intelligent design with some scientific rigor and determine how life adapts to the environment.

Robert Affolter, D.C.

Exposed

How Politics Increased the Cost of Health Care in America

Preface

Societal evolution over the last 100 years has changed many ways we think and behave. Our health care system has also evolved over the last 100 years. While an undergraduate student in the mid 1970s, I wrote a paper on health maintenance organizations. At that time it was a little known concept and most people talked about medical care not health care.

Today our politicians are talking about access to health care. By that they mean having an insurance policy. It galls me to hear that access to health care is no longer about whether or not a sick person can get in to see a doctor but merely whether or not the person has insurance. Politicians don't seem to understand that people can be financially bled with insurance premiums to the point that they can't afford the deductibles and co-pays. They can't see a doctor, even though by the politicians' standards they have health care.

While writing this book I realized that I actually have two points. One point is that health care costs are going up because government intervention has limited supply while encouraging demand and favored insurance and drug companies over private citizens, this book. The second point is that health care costs are going up based on a false philosophy of science of life. The second point is covered in the companion book, Exposed – The "Science" of Medicine and the Dollars It Generates.

It is my hope that the two books will contribute to the debate about our health care system. I encourage us to place removing the impediments to health ahead of corporate welfare, whether the corporation is an insurance company, hospital, pharmaceutical company, or private clinic.

Contents

Introduction

First lady, Hillary Clinton was working on a national health care plan and Washington State was determined to be the leader of the nation. Our legislators called a town hall meeting. I showed up and after a short introduction, one of our legislators asked for input from the audience.

I stood up and asked a couple of questions. "First we must be clear. We are talking about reducing the cost of seeing a doctor. Is that true?"

The legislator nodded.

"What do you think would happen to the cost of a doctor visit if you went back to the legislature tomorrow and made health insurance illegal?"

The legislator appeared dumbfounded.

From the back of the room a man shouted, "It would drop in a hell of a hurry. I'll tell you that."

Later I found that man. He was a retired thoracic surgeon.

This story points out a couple of points. It seems obvious that if every doctor in the nation and all the pharmaceutical companies had to compete for the dollar in your pocket, costs would come down.

It also seems obvious that if you had to pay for your care out of your pocket, you would be more careful about your health care purchases. I've seen many people who have insurance and still cannot afford to see a doctor. Or, even more frequent are the people who think if the insurance company won't pay they can't afford to take care of their health. Often, it is a simple matter of priority.

I remember one person who gave me the sob story about how insurance wouldn't cover her care, then left my office and climbed into a huge pickup pulling a trailer with two jet skis. The family was off to the lake.

I had another family who was covered by our state's Medicaid program. When the program cut chiropractic care they told me they didn't know how they would make it without care. I was naïve enough to open my clinic an hour early and ran by donation for one hour. They couldn't get out of bed early enough to come in.

Should we pay for health care for people who do not value their health? Should we allow doctors to negotiate directly with patients to make health care affordable? Do you even know that our legal system makes it illegal for your doctor to reduce fees for you? How did we get here? What role has government played in driving up the cost of health care?

I'm going to tell you why your physician or hospital is charging so much. I'm going to tell you why your insurance company gets a discount while those without insurance are sent to collections for the whole amount. I'm going to tell you why big pharmaceutical and the insurance industry are the winners and the average American is losing. I'm going to show you the role our government is playing in the rising cost of health care.

Health Care Economics:
What happened to the Law of Supply and Demand?

Application of the basic supply and demand curves can often shed light on market dynamics. Although the graph below is simplistic, it will help make some basic points.

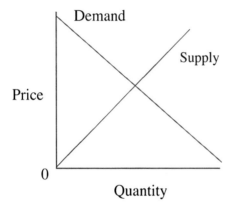

The Demand line shows that as price decreases more people buy so the quantity purchased increases. The Supply line shows that as price increases the quantity supplied increases. Where the two lines cross is the equilibrium price.

If there is high demand for something and supply is restricted, suppliers will hold out for a higher price. Price increases. As price increases, more people will be attracted to be suppliers and, if supply is not constrained, supply will increase. As supply increases the demand is filled and supply will exceed demand. Buyers will begin to shop around. Suppliers are then forced to lower price to increase demand. The back and forth oscillation between supply and demand would be the natural expectation in a free market.

If supply were artificially constrained, we would expect price to be higher than equilibrium. If demand were artificially stimulated, we would expect price to be higher than equilibrium.

Politicians have artificially increased demand and decreased supply, all under the banner of protecting the public. We are now being told that health care costs are out of control and government intervention is the solution.

How did this occur? First, we must look at the start of government intervention – vaccination.

The First Government Intervention:
Mandatory Vaccination

It doesn't take long for free people to decide that their health might require mandatory sacrifice of others. Massachusetts passed the first mandatory vaccination law in 1809.[1] The required vaccine was for small pox.

A big boost to vaccination came from the polio vaccine in 1955. In fact, the CDC begins the vaccination timeline with the polio vaccine. [2] That was also when we began to see advanced statistical analysis to show that treatments or vaccination programs worked.

The efficacy of vaccination programs will be discussed in the companion book. Suffice it to say that mandatory vaccination drove up the demand for medical care.

Note that demand was not driven up by obvious results. People did not trust vaccination programs. The government mandated it.

In Washington State, the *required* vaccinations for admission to kindergarten are: Hepatitis B, diphtheria, tetanus and pertussis, measles, mumps, rubella, polio and varicella. The vaccination programs encourage young parents to believe that children cannot be healthy without the services of their physician.

However, our politicians have gone even further than that. People have been taken to court for turning to God, prayer, or utilizing other than the state sponsored methods of treatment. The most recent, nationally known case involved a teenager who fled his hometown after a court order to take toxic medicines to treat his lymphoma. [3]

All this legal maneuvering is supposedly to save lives. Whether it does or not may be in question. There is no question that our government drives up demand for health care.

Cutting Supply:
State Endorsed Health System

As the nineteenth century rolled to the twentieth, there were many different branches of so-called health care. Chiropractors, homeopaths, naturopaths, allopaths, osteopaths, ophthalmologists, and podiatrists are some of the more prevalent branches that have succeeded in some manner today.

A research scholar at the Carnegie Foundation for the Advancement of Teaching, Abraham Flexner, wrote a paper critical of the state of medical education in America. The Flexner Report in 1910 criticized the state of medical training. The German allopathic curriculum was advocated as the standard. [4]

The Federal and state governments adopted the new standards. Only those schools that adopted the new standard were given research funds. State licensing boards would only license doctors that graduated from the standardized schools. Through research funding, standardizing medical school curriculum, and state licensing boards supply has been limited. Not only was supply of physicians limited, thought was limited by artificially constraining treatment methodologies. [5]

The preferred methods were not determined by scientific studies, but by government intervention. Indeed, modern day statistical analysis using randomized controlled trials would not be the norm for several decades. The allopathic approach was chosen for its appeal as being scientific.

While many other approaches based treatment on working with life, the allopath based the approach on controlling the organism. Life was the result of evolution, the random interaction of particles of matter. Through scientific studies, doctors could learn to understand the body and control it. If the body deviated from a perceived normal, the allopath would give the patient something to normalize function. That was deemed "scientific" medicine.

Science was making great strides. Atheists were pushing the theory of evolution and the religious conservatives were pushing back. Science was winning the intellectual argument.

The point here is not whether allopathic medicine is right or wrong, that is dealt with in the companion book. The point here is that supply was constrained. The Flexner report called for fewer medical schools, increased entrance requirements, stiffer curriculum, and association of schools with teaching hospitals. [6]

The Flexner report also had the effect of increasing the status of allopathic medical physicians. They had been advocating increased academic standards to improve their image. The "arduous and expensive" [7] curriculum proposed by Flexner was just what the doctors ordered.

However, Flexner was just one battle in the assault of atheists against religious conservatives. Thanks to government intervention through funding and licensing, the medical profession became under control of the allopaths. Remember that it happened by controlling medical education. The first step is to control thought.

Next was assault on the education of school children. The battle line was drawn in Dayton, Kentucky in 1925.

The Scopes Monkey Trial

Controlling the education system is a key aspect of government control of our lives. What we believe from an early age, we tend not to question.

Seeing what was coming, the Kentucky legislature passed a law making it illegal to teach evolution in the public schools. Leaders of the town of Dayton, Kentucky decided to challenge the law to increase business. [8]

Mr. Scopes was teaching evolution as part of a biology class and agreed to challenge the law. The trial became known as the Scopes Monkey Trial, for the assertion that man descended from monkeys. The trial was the basis for the movie *Inherit the Wind.* [9]

The outcome of the trial was less important than the arguments presented. The literal interpretation of the Bible was questioned. Although Scopes was convicted, evolution was taught in public schools and the law was never challenged again.

Children are taught that evolution is the scientific and therefore true explanation of the beginnings of life. If we can get children to question belief in God, if they believe that life is merely random chance events, they will be more likely to turn to their physician when they become sick adults.

By teaching random interaction of matter as the beginning of life, all modes of healing that utilized what is now called intelligent design were not only called into question, they were labeled as unscientific. That had the effect of further curtailing demand and supply of services other than allopathic medicine.

So far we have seen the role of government in reducing the supply of physicians and increasing demand for services. What if the physicians did not have to confront the patient for payment? What if the patient did not have to pay the physician? We would have utopia/insurance.

Health Insurance - A Misnomer

Insurance originally was created as compensation for loss. Two things affect the premium. One is the degree of risk of loss. If the risk is high, the premium should be high. If the risk is low, the premium should be lower. The second thing that affects premium is the amount of the loss itself. If the amount is high, the premium is high. If the amount is low, the premium should be lower.

Car insurance pays if you have an accident. If you drive recklessly, you will pay a higher premium. If you drive an expensive car you will pay more to insure your car. Increased risk and increased possible loss is easy to understand.

The case is similar for homeowner's insurance. You insure your home in case something bad happens to your house. Fire is the most common. Insurance doesn't pay for you to paint your house every five years. It doesn't pay for you to put a new roof on it. It may not even pay if you have a flood. If there is a fire, your insurance will probably pay.

Life insurance is really death insurance. It pays when the covered person dies. Insurance companies may require a physical exam to determine the risk of death and the resulting payout.

What about health insurance? It used to cover risk of loss. It paid for medical care if you became ill or got hurt. It didn't cover all risks and it didn't try to reduce risks. I remember talking with an agent when my wife and I were young. He explained that adding obstetrics care would cost more. We paid more to have pregnancy covered.

In an effort to sell more policies, insurance companies began covering things that were supposed to keep you healthy. A certain number of wellness massage visits, acupuncture, chiropractic, etc. were allowed every year. In addition, health club memberships were sometimes covered.

Where is the risk of loss? The Office of the Insurance Commissioner regulates insurance companies. Why did the Insurance Commissioner allow insurance companies to offer services for health promotion?

The reason is public demand. A former executive director of our Washington State Chiropractic Association told me that he met the president of a large insurance company at a social function. The director pulled the president aside and told him that chiropractic care could save his company a lot of money in treating their subscribers. His reply: "I don't care what will save us money on the back end. I want to know what will sell policies on the front end."

Allowing insurance companies to offer coverage for wellness care blurred the difference between what should be covered by insurance and what should not be covered. People thought it was a great idea that their insurance company wanted them to stay healthy. Costs continued to rise.

If we want the cost of health insurance to go down, we have to go back to covering risk of loss for covered conditions. We must realize that health insurance does not pay for everything. It does cover certain treatments for covered conditions.

What conditions are covered and what treatments are reimbursed should be a matter of science – not politics. However, the problem is that politicians have already rigged the system. Research funding goes primarily to allopathic medicine. The fix is in and costs continue to rise, because health insurance is not about health or insurance. It is about getting your money.

Why the Cost of Health Care Rose So Fast

When I began practice in the 1980s, some patients had insurance. They would pay me and submit their receipts to the insurance company for reimbursement. The idea was simple. The patient had a contract with me to provide care. The patient had a contract with the insurance company to reimburse the patient for care. I had no contract with the insurance company.

The insurance company didn't pay the entire bill. They paid a percentage of what was "usual and customary". How did they decide what was "usual and customary"? They looked at last year's bills.

You don't have to be a member of the brightest profession in America to realize that if you want the "usual and customary fee" to increase next year, you better raise your fee this year. The cost of medical care grew much faster than inflation.

Add to that the attitude of patients. I remember one patient who said, "Charge them as much as you can doc. You're worth it."

There was no incentive to keep costs down. Who gains if the cost of a doctor visit is actually affordable? Would you buy insurance if you knew you could afford to pay the doctor or hospital if you needed to? I doubt if anyone would.

Doctors, hospitals and drug companies make more money with higher fees because the insurance company pays the bill. Demand does not fall with higher fees because the patient feels entitled to care. Patients feel that they are finally getting something for that premium they pay every month. The insurance company should pay. Who cares how much it costs?

The insurance company wants you to fear a high bill so you will continue to pay premiums. The entire system is built on soaking the consumer for as high a premium as possible and the doctors charging the insurance company as much as possible.

Something had to give.

Insurance Company Panel Doctors

Our government allowed the insurance companies to contract with doctors. The contracts could be worded in various ways but the gist of it was that the doctors agreed to a lower fee in return for more patients.

The cash patient without insurance has really been ripped off. In order to understand why, I need to fill in a few more details.

We (doctors) have been told that it is illegal to charge an insurance company more than we would charge a cash patient for the same service. I'm not an attorney and I don't know if the law is federal, state or established by court.

At first thought it makes sense that a doctor shouldn't be allowed to charge an insurance company more. However, the increased costs are enormous. Billing the insurance company is easy. Keeping track of whether or not the bill got paid and rebilling or sending the remainder to the patient is time consuming. In addition the insurance companies often want copies of notes or reports. It all drives up costs.

Then, add to those costs the time value of money. If a patient pays cash today, I can begin to earn interest on the money. Or, at least I can pay my bills and not pay interest on credit cards. The insurance company can delay payment for months and earn interest on the money that I should have been paid. Obviously, fifty dollars today is worth more than fifty dollars six months from now.

So, how do hospitals and physicians make up for the extra cost of billing insurance if they can't charge the insurance company more? Did a light go on? They charge the cash patient more.

Since the doctor's costs go up because of dealing with insurance, and since the insurance company will only pay the cash fee, guess what? The cash patient must pay the insurance company fee. Then the true cost of billing the insurance can be passed on to the insurance company.

The cash patient must pay more to subsidize the cost of billing insurance. Insulted yet? Try this.

Now the doctor contracts with the insurance company to become a "panel doctor" and take a lower fee, what the insurance company calls the "allowed amount". We are told that courts have decreed that we can lower our fee for two reasons: 1) a bookkeeping discount for cash at time of service, and 2) volume discount. The insurance companies get a volume discount.

Remember when President George W Bush said that he was going to make the doctors agreements with insurance companies public record so you could negotiate your fee down? Are you surprised that it didn't happen? The doctor has no choice. The cash patient must be charged the higher fee.

Many people didn't like the panel doctor approach because they couldn't see the doctor of their choice. So preferred provider organizations came into the mix.

Preferred Provider Organizations – PPO

A PPO is an association or company of health care professionals. The professionals have agreed to provide services for a lowered fee to subscribers of insurance companies that have contracts with the PPO.

Remember the two contracts I wrote about earlier? One was the contract between the insurance company and the patient. The other contract was between the patient and the provider.

Now the provider has a contract with the PPO. The PPO has a contract with the insurance company. The insurance company has a contract with the patient.

Providers who are members of the PPO are considered "preferred providers" or "in-network." Providers who are not members are "out-of-network".

Typically the insurance policy has a lower deductible and co-pay for going to a doctor who is a member of the PPO. A common contract is something like this: If the patient sees a PPO provider, the patient just has a $25 co-pay. Co-pay is the amount of the fee that the patient must pay. The insurance company pays the balance of the fee after the co-pay. If the patient sees an out of network provider, the insurance company might pay 60% of the allowed amount.

So in the above example, if my fee is $47 and I am in-network, the patient will pay the $25 co-pay. The insurance company would pay the balance of $22. If I am out-of-network the insurance company will pay 60% of the allowed amount. If the allowed amount is $47, the insurance company would pay $28.20 and the patient would pay $18.80. There would be no incentive for the patient or for me to be in network.

More commonly the allowed amount is much less. If the allowed amount is $26, the patient still pays $25 if I am in network and the insurance company pays $1. If I am out-of-network, the insurance company pays $15.60 (60% of $26 allowed amount) and the patient pays $31.40.

Notice that the only thing that makes any sense from the doctor's or patient's point of view is for the fee to be much higher. It seems like you are getting something for your money if you pay a $25 co-pay for a $100 office visit. If the allowed amount was $100, the insurance company would pay $60 and the patient would pay $40 to an out-of-network provider. There would be an incentive for the patient to see an in-network provider and only pay the $25 co-pay.

The above examples are not only real. They are common. The other thing that is becoming more common is to have a high deductible. The deductible is the amount the patient must pay before the insurance company pays anything. It is not uncommon for a patient to have a $1500 or as high as $4000 deductible.

The allowed amount also applies to the deductible. In the above examples, if my fee is $47, the allowed amount is $26, and the deductible is $500, the insurance company will only count $26 of the $47 fee toward the deductible. After 11 office visits, the patient will have paid me $517 (11 x $47). The insurance company will only count $286 (11 x $26) toward the deductible.

Even more aggravating is the insurance policy with a deductible and a maximum number of office visits. In the above example, if the patient has a 12 visit per year maximum, the insurance company will not pay any chiropractic claims because the visit per year maximum will be reached before the deductible is met.

I recently received an offer from a new network. Their fee schedule offers to pay me 70% of my usual and customary fee or $40 whichever is lower. My fee is $47. If I accept the terms of the network, I will receive $28 (.7 times $47). In order to receive the full $40 I would have to raise my usual and customary fee to $57 ($47 divided by .7). Should I raise my fee to cash paying patients so that I can receive the maximum from the network? Remember that the maximum from the network is only 85% ($40 divided by $47) of my usual and customary fee.

The above gives you some idea of the complexities of working with different insurance companies and different policies. The bottom line is this: most patients are paying more cash, which I've heard is the Canadian system.

I was attending a seminar a couple of years ago and met a chiropractor from Canada. I asked him how their system worked. He replied, "Great. Everybody knows the system doesn't pay and they pay cash."

Do You Take My Insurance?

That is often the first question a prospective patient asks. They seem to liken the question to asking if we take major credit cards. The confusion is understandable. The patient presents a plastic card, just like a credit card, and expects the fees to be paid.

Most patients pay little to no attention to the EOB, Explanation of Benefits, which comes from the insurance company. The EOB tells just how much your doctor charged, how much the insurance paid and how much the patient owes. Most patients look at the part of the EOB that says how much the patient owes. They might even look at how much the doctor charges. They rarely look at how much the insurance company actually paid.

One insurance company will usually have many different policies. Calling your doctor's office and stating that you have coverage with a certain insurance company means nothing. Knowing who your employer is will often help identify the policy.

Imagine keeping track of all the different insurance companies and all the different policies. It could be a full time job. In fact, many doctors have now joined clinics that have billing departments that spend all day billing insurance and verifying coverage. All that drives up the cost of health care.

What About Medicare?

I've heard journalists say that everyone loves Medicare. We should just expand Medicare benefits for all.

Ask the doctors if they love it.

For the last few years, it seems that every year Medicare cuts the physician fee schedule. When I began practice in 1985 my cash office fee was $25. My memory is that Medicare paid about $17. Today Medicare pays about $19 for the same service. My fee is $47.

I don't think medical physicians have it any different. Faced with rising costs and diminished reimbursements, many are no longer taking Medicare patients. When my mother moved to town, there was only one clinic taking Medicare patients. That clinic specializes in Medicare.

A colleague told me that he was no longer going to accept Medicare patients. His analysis: "It takes them twice as long to get on the table. Every time they come in they want to tell you their whole life story. If you tell them what they really need to get well, they think you are trying to rip off Medicare. It just isn't worth it."

I enjoy helping the elderly. Often times they have given up hope of feeling better and are very grateful to be able to walk and move better. However, they do pose a challenge for those of us running a clinic.

Why do medical costs continue to rise even though the insurance company reimbursement rates are going down? The answer is more procedures.

A good example is my mother. She fainted in an airport. She has fainted before and chiropractic care seems to help. Understandably, the airline wanted her to go to the hospital. The physicians decided to keep her overnight for observation and tests. The next day she was allowed to leave with no treatment necessary. The battery of tests and over- night room cost $10,000.

Although it is infuriating, I find it difficult to fault the physicians. Medicare continues to cut the fees for service and in retaliation they perform more services. If we assume the physicians were honest, my mother received a very thorough exam and knows that there is nothing to be done from a medical perspective.

Some claim that is an example of the American health care system at its best. She was in the hospital quickly. She received a lot of expensive tests. If something had been found, they might have saved her life. On the other hand, if medical care really is the third leading cause of death, [10] perhaps she was lucky to get out alive.

More Tests, More Care – Is It Needed?

Doctors and hospitals have to cover their costs. If the reimbursement rates go down they must perform more procedures to make up the difference.

President Obama recently said that we will have to get used to having fewer tests and that doctors will get paid for helping people get well.

I agree with him in sentiment. How do we accomplish his objective? How will providers prove that treatment was necessary without before and after objective measurement? Will patient satisfaction surveys be enough?

For many years now I have pointed out that no health care professional believes that you can tell how healthy you are by how you feel. The medical profession advocates pap smears, mammograms, blood pressure tests, cholesterol tests, etc. The acupuncturists might look at your tongue or feel pulses. The chiropractors check spinal motion and a range of other tests. Those are just a few examples. What tests should we pay for?

The problem is that many of us base our entire practice approach on the tests we have come to trust. We use them to determine how to manage a patient and assess the patient's response to care. Sure surveys are important, but many of us would feel disoriented if we were forced to give up our favorite tests.

Licensing of Providers – Protecting the Public?

We assume that a licensed health care provider is more competent than someone who is not licensed. To obtain a license a provider must first complete the required training and then pass an examination.

What about corporations? A corporation is a separate legal entity created by the government. A corporation cannot be trained or take an examination. In Washington State, health care providers can form a special form of corporation called a professional service corporation. All owners of the corporation must be licensed in one of the listed professions. The idea seems to be that everyone has a license to lose and will have an incentive to act ethically.

Imagine if a corporation could be formed and the owners did not have to be licensed. The owners could just hire licensed professionals and require that they behave in an unethical manner. When the professional lost his/her license, the corporation could just hire another professional and continue business.

It is interesting how often it seems that licensing laws are not enforced. I'm sure there must be some legal loophole that allows school districts to practice medicine by hiring nurses, corporations to hire their own physicians, hospitals to hire doctors, etc.

The Stark Laws make it illegal for a doctor to refer a patient to a facility in which she/he owns a financial interest.[11] The laws are thought to reduce costs by not allowing a doctor to make additional money by referring a patient for more care.

Yet hospitals across the nation are buying medical practices. Somehow they seem to be practicing medicine without a license and for some reason politicians must consider owners of a hospital to be more ethical than the doctors.

Or, could it be that owners of hospitals have more money and contribute more to political campaigns?

Insurance Companies Practicing Medicine

One day I was talking with a claims manager. Claims managers work for the insurance companies and determine what claims get paid. This particular claims manager told me that she could control whether my patient saw me or not.

I replied that the decision to see me is between my patient and me. She could only control whether the insurance company paid for it or not.

Think about it. If the insurance company can decide whether or not a patient can see a doctor, or if the insurance company can decide whether or not to pay for a given treatment, isn't the insurance company practicing medicine? Can the insurance company be sued for practicing medicine without a license?

The answers are of course and of course not. It seems obvious that the insurance company is practicing medicine. So I wondered, why aren't we suing the insurance companies? The answer: In Washington State any company that comes under the auspices of the Insurance Commissioner cannot be sued for practicing medicine without a license. If they aren't practicing medicine, the companies cannot be sued for malpractice either.

The politicians allowed the insurance companies to practice medicine and protected the insurance companies from poor decisions. At the same time, the politicians made it illegal for doctors to offer insurance.

Future Care Plans Determined to Be Insurance

When I began practice in the mid 1980s, many chiropractors I knew had individual and family wellness plans. The patients would pay us a fixed amount every month and could come in for care as often as they wanted.

In Washington State, the insurance commissioner ruled that future care contracts were insurance. The idea was that by offering unlimited care for a fixed fee, doctors were assuming the risk of future injury. The concept seems accurate. Doctors probably were offering insurance. Was the public being damaged? People who already knew that they wanted regular chiropractic checkups were signing up for care at a reduced fee. Isn't that what we want?

No! The politicians ruled that you couldn't get reduced fees to go to your doctor unless the insurance company gets a cut first.

To really understand how crooked that is, let me explain capitation of fees. If a doctor signs a contract with a Health Maintenance Organization, the contract can specify that the doctor will be paid a flat fee to serve each of the members of the HMO. That is called a capitation agreement. [12] So, what was illegal for the doctor to do for you as an individual is perfectly fine as long as the insurance company or HMO gets a cut of the cash.

Remember, it is okay for the insurance company to practice medicine and cover activities where no risk was involved. It was not okay for a health care provider to assume a small risk and give patients a break.

Does our government care more about individual health or big money?

Mandated Benefits – Are They Driving Up Costs?

I heard a so-called conservative say that health care competition in Washington State has been reduced to about 6 insurance companies from around 100 because of mandated benefits.

He failed to recognize that competition had been reduced from thousands of doctors to the 100 insurance companies before mandated benefits. The reduced competition occurred because of government intervention.

Mandated benefits are services that have been required by the government to be put in insurance policies. Chiropractic, massage, acupuncture, and psychiatry are examples of services that may be mandated.

When I started practice, I remember a patient who came to me for back pain. He was faced with a choice: Pay $300 dollars out of his pocket to me for exam, x-rays and a trial of care. Or, his insurance would cover the CAT scan his M.D. recommended for $800 with no out of pocket.

Where was the level playing field?

I'm not familiar with all mandated benefits. I am privy to what happens when chiropractic care is offered as a choice.

A chiropractic web site article reviewed four studies published in 2004. [13]

One of the research articles reviewed data from insurance records comparing patients with a chiropractic benefit to those without. The results? Those with chiropractic coverage had 41% fewer hospitalizations for back pain, 37% less MRIs, 23% fewer x-rays, and 32% fewer surgeries.

Tough Choices Ahead
Is Death the Enemy?

Back in the 1980s, an elderly patient told me a story about the death of her grandmother. Her grandmother had become quite ill and a doctor was called out to the house. After examination, the doctor said that she needed an operation. She would have to go to the hospital. The operation would cost about $100.

Her grandmother looked at her grandfather and said, "I don't know. What do you think?"

He said, "I don't know. What do you think?"

She replied, "Well, I don't think I'm worth it."

He said, "Yeah. I reckon not."

That was a tough choice. It is one thing to make the choice for myself. I wouldn't want to make the decision for someone else. Yet, our government will be forced to make those decisions, if government takes over health care.

The amount of money spent on health care in the last few months of life is enormous. We have some tough choices to make. Should we pay twenty thousand dollars in high tech medical care to keep one person alive for a few more months, often confined to a hospital bed or nursing home? Or, is that same money better spent on low-tech procedures, like chiropractic, to help ten people walk and function better, for a year?

I've heard that it has been proposed that more people will have to choose hospice care, under government run health care. That would be one way to reduce costs. Otherwise, the sky is the limit.

Single Payer Health Care

If we adopt a single payer system, will the system cover all care for all circumstances? What will happen to the state worker's compensation system? Will employers pay less in worker's compensation taxes because the state no longer has to pay for health care?

Will the single payer system pay to treat those injured in automobile accidents? Will auto insurance fees go down because the insurance companies no longer have to pay for health care?

What will happen to jury verdicts in liability cases? Will the verdicts go down because health care is guaranteed and not paid by the patient? Will my homeowner's policy premium go down due to the reduced liability?

There may be a lot of benefits and unintended consequences if we have a single payer system. It is difficult to see how it will reduce health care costs.

I've heard it said that we need a public option to keep the health insurance companies honest. Is that an honest statement? Medicare can mandate that I bill Medicare for covered services and tell me what I can charge. How can private insurance compete with that?

As long as there is a deep pocket of money and a disconnect between the providers and patients, more care will be prescribed.

Conclusion

Government has driven up the cost of health care by favoring the insurance and pharmaceutical industries. Government policies have reduced supply and increased, even mandated, demand.

Government regulation forbids providers from charging insurance companies more than patients without insurance. Cash patients are forced to subsidize the cost of insurance.

It should be obvious that the most cost effective means of paying for the services of a health care provider is for the patient to pay. Direct payment by patients should be encouraged and cash patients should not have to subsidize the cost of billing insurance.

The playing field should be even without mandating services of one provider type over another, unless science warrants it. Patients should be allowed the treatment of their choice.

If the government adopts a catastrophic plan (true insurance for major illness or injury) with health savings accounts to cover more minor problems, qualified expenses should be broader than allopathic medicine.

We need to change our thinking. Death is not the ultimate enemy. Quality of life needs to be stressed. Government support of allopathic medicine has gotten us where we are. It is time to re-evaluate.

Bibliography

1. Welborn, Angie A. Mandatory Vaccinations: Precedent and Current Laws. CRS Report for Congress, CRS Web order code RJ21414 updated 18 January 2005 accessed 07/21/2009 http://www.fas.org/sgp/crs/RS21414.pdf

2. Vaccines and Immunizations. Publication: Vaccine Timeline. Department of Health and Human Services Centers for Disease Control and Prevention, 19 October 2006 Accessed 07/21/2009
http://www.cdc.gov/vaccines/pubs/vacc-timeline.htm

3. Boy who fled chemo may be headed to Mexico. MSNBC Health/Kids and Parenting. 25 May 2009. Accessed 07/21/2009
http://www.msnbc.msn.com/id/30824587/

4. Beck, AH. The Flexner Report and the Standardization of American Medical Education. JAMA. 2004:291(17):2139-2140. accessed 06/27/09
http://jama.ama-assn.org/cgi/reprint/291/17/2139

5. Ibid.

6. Ibid.

7. Ibid.

8. Linder, Douglas O. State v. John Scopes ("The Monkey Trial"). University of Missouri-Kansas City. accessed 07/10/09
http://www.law.umkc.edu/faculty/projects/Ftrials/scopes/evolut.htm

9. Ibid.

10. Starfield, Barbara, America's Healthcare System is the Third Leading Cause of Death. http://www.health-care-reform.net/causedeath.htm accessed 07/10/09

11. "Stark Law". Wikipedia updated 6 June 1009. accessed 07/22/09
http://en.wikipedia.org/wiki/Stark_Law

12. Montgomery, Kelly. About.com:Health Insurance Capitation. 10 June 2005 accessed 07/21/2009
http://healthinsurance.about.com/od/glossary/g/capitation.htm

13. "Chiropractic Again Shown to Be More Cost Effective." Dynamic Chiropractic 30 Nov 2004; Vol 22 Issue 25. Chiroweb.com accessed on 07/22/09
http://www.chiroweb.com/mpacms/dc/article.php?id=46534

Exposed:
The "Science" of Medicine and
The Dollars It Generates

Preface

This book is a companion book to Exposed: How Politics Increased the Cost of Health Care In America. This book looks at the philosophy and science of allopathic medicine, its atheistic premise, evolutionary roots, and how it has come to be the orthodox system in America. I will also give evidence for basing health care on intelligent design.

This book asks you to question everything you think you know. I am providing references for statements so that the inquiring reader can look up the references and make rational decisions.

The companion book is a book of my experience of nearly a quarter century in the field as a practicing chiropractor. It shows how government intervention has favored insurance companies and drug companies. It has driven up the cost of health care and made it illegal for your doctor to give you a break, but legal for your doctor to give an insurance company a discount.

Together these two books paint a rather disconcerting picture of what has happened to our health care system in America. I hope it is not too late to wake up and make some real changes.

Contents

Introduction

Medical care is the third leading cause of death in America.[1] Yet; we can't get enough of it. Congress is being pushed to pass legislation making it easier for more people to have access to care.

Proponents of single payer health care point to statistics in other countries that have socialized systems. Proponents claim, among other things, that longevity is higher and infant mortality is lower in those countries.

Opponents of single payer health care claim we will receive less care and will be placed on waiting lists for tests, procedures and surgeries. Could both proponents and opponents be right? Is it possible that people in those countries with socialized medicine actually receive less care and are healthier?

A long time ago I read an article about medical research. The author stated that drug companies put research and development under the marketing department. The reason was that it was important to determine what question research and development should answer.

As I remember, the example was researching the question: What medication can prevent a second heart attack? If a successful drug could be found, the market would be people who had recovered from a heart attack.

However, if the question was: What medication can prevent the first heart attack? The market would be everybody.

Imagine a medication that made you feel better but never made you well. You'd be a customer for life, but you would only need that one medication. It would be like taking aspirin for a headache.

Now imagine that a medication would make your symptom go away but cause another problem, like taking aspirin for a headache and getting intestinal bleeding. Now you need additional medical care for the side effects of the first. The cascade begins.

Let's go a step further. What if you don't even feel bad but I can convince you that you need a medication to prevent premature death? It would be like taking aspirin every day to prevent heart attack or stroke. Now we are just beginning to get the picture of what is wrong with "health care" in America.

To fix the problem, we have to look at our system with a critical eye. We have to go beyond the standard line that says "Americans have the best health system in the world" and question that statement.

Can we improve our health care? Can we have a system based on truth rather than marketing spin? I think we can.

To improve the quality of life of Americans, we have to determine the cause of health and scientifically test outcomes. Every science begins with philosophy. We must begin with the philosophy of orthodox, allopathic, or evolution-based medicine and re-visit the alternative.

Falsification, the Basis of Science

Philosopher of science Karl Popper is credited with emphasizing the power of falsification. We can never prove that something is true. No matter how much evidence we have that something is true there is always the possibility that a new observation will contradict the theory.

Stephen Hawking wrote that just a single observation that contradicts a theory is enough to discard the theory and advance science.[2] Science uses the falsification process to prove theories wrong and when failing to do so, the failure adds evidence for the truth of the theory.

As we shall see orthodox, allopathic, evolution-based medicine does not meet the standards of science as proposed by Stephen Hawking. In fact rather than allowing one observation to falsify a hypothesis, we find "scientific" medicine treating patients when the hypothesis is falsified 98% of the time. Imagine the money to be made when 98% of the patients treated will not be benefited by the treatment.

I am not anti-medicine or surgery. In fact, I hope we all agree that medication to relieve pain and suffering is a benefit to mankind. I hope we also agree that surgery to put people back together or correct a defect also benefits mankind. However, much of the medical care claimed to prevent disease is based on statistical nonsense. It is time to expose this pseudoscientific, statistical nonsense for what it really is.

Science vs. Religion

In June of 2003 I had the pleasure of corresponding by email with a group of medical professionals and self-proclaimed alternative care skeptics. It is our detractors who help make us strong by challenging our beliefs and sharpening our skills.

One of the lights that came on during that discussion was that medicine is based entirely on atheism. That does not mean that every medical practitioner is an atheist. However, if the practitioner is practicing orthodox, allopathic, evolution-based medicine he or she is practicing atheism.

To understand how we got here, it is important to understand the choice that we had in health care nearly 100 years ago. The following definitions are paraphrased from my old Webster's dictionary. Although other forms of practice were also in place, the following are still active in some form today.

Allopath: a system of medical practice that treats disease by giving substances that in normal persons would produce symptoms different than the symptoms being treated; conventional medicine except homeopathy[3]

Chiropractic: a system of healing using adjustment of body structure to restore normal nerve function[4]

Homeopathy: a system of medical practice that treats a disease by giving small doses of substances that in normal persons would produce the same symptoms as those being treated[5]

Naturopathy: a system of treatment of disease

emphasizing working with nature[6]

The naturopath assists nature. The homeopath alerts the body with low doses of something that would have produced the same symptom as the symptom being treated. The chiropractic method works with the nervous system to allow innate intelligence to heal the body. The allopath denies any intelligence behind the function of the body. There is the sharp distinction between "scientific" medicine and many of the methods of alternative practitioners, the recognition of intelligence.

I've read that medical doctors don't like the term allopath. Instead I'm going to refer to them as evolution-based medicine, doctors who deny intelligent design.

How did one group gain control and nearly crush all other branches of health care? Was it the advancement of science? Was it clinical superiority? Nope. It was politics and money.

The American Medical Association (AMA) tried to standardize medical school curriculum and reduce the number of schools for nearly half a century. In 1904, they formed the Council on Medical Education. With help from the Carnegie Foundation for Advancement of Teaching, a study was undertaken to determine the state of medical education in the United States. The result was the Flexner Report published in 1910. Abraham Flexner, author of the report, stated that medical education should be "arduous and expensive." [7]

The standards that were adopted were much as today. Medical school was entered after completing a prerequisite program of study. The first two years of medical school were basic sciences and the second two years were working in a teaching hospital.

It was argued that the government should not waste resources on colleges that did not have the financial capabilities to provide the necessary education. Money was only given to schools adopting the new standards. Soon, state-licensing boards would only license graduates of approved schools.

While it is argued that the push was to make medicine more scientific we must place the statement in context of what it means to be scientific. Evolutionary theory was just taking hold. Fifteen years later, 1925, the Scopes trial would bring the issue of teaching evolution in the public schools to the forefront. The teaching of creationism in public schools won the trial but lost in the court of public opinion. [8]

Now, the evolutionary theory stating that intelligence evolved unguided from matter has been taught as truth for so long that any other idea is ridiculed. Evolutionists are now in positions of power throughout government. They determine who gets research funding. Any method that does not meet their approval does not get funding. Methods that meet their approval get funding. They then abuse their power by claiming that there is no research evidence to support positions adversarial to their own.

With all this emphasis on science and all the money dumped into medicine and evolutionary research, medical procedures are now supported by solid scientific evidence, right? No.

A cover story in BusinessWeek was titled Medical

Guesswork. The article was about the work of Dr. David Eddy using statistics to improve medical outcomes. Dr. Eddy holds a clinical doctorate in medicine as well as a doctor of philosophy in statistics. According to the article, although things are improving, as of 2006, only 20-25% of medicine was supported by solid evidence. [9]

Science and Religion – Still Entangled

Where I live the hospital is named Saint Joseph. A patient is encouraged to pray and receive medical care. The Catholics who run the hospital claim they are carrying on the healing mission of Jesus Christ. I can find no evidence that Jesus Christ resorted to pills or surgery. It is an interesting contradiction.

The self-proclaimed skeptics that I mentioned earlier criticized chiropractic as unscientific for basing care on innate intelligence. Yet, "scientific" medicine practices in hospitals run by a religion.

A physician can practice medicine in a non-evolution-based manner. A physician can recognize the intelligence of life and recognize intelligent design. However, by so doing, he is no longer practicing "scientific" medicine. After my wife's surgery, her gynecologist told her that if she felt nauseous and did not feel like eating, that was God telling her not to eat. A less enlightened evolutionist would have given her a drug for the nausea and encouraged her to eat.

One of my favorite stories is the patient who came to me one day for a spinal checkup. She told me that she had nausea and diarrhea and thought she should see her medical physician. I agreed.

On her next visit I asked if she had seen her doctor. She said, "Yes. He thinks I have an intestinal virus."

"What does he propose to do about it?"

She rummaged through her purse and presented two bottles of pills, one in each hand. "This one is for the nausea and this one is for the diarrhea."

"That is why I could never be a medical doctor."

"What do you mean?"

"Let's assume he is right. You have an intestinal virus and your body is trying to throw it out both ends. Your doctor is trying to keep it in there. It just makes no sense."

It would be nice if the treatments actually fit the diagnosis and helped the patient become healthy rather than merely making the patient feel better.

If we are to improve our health care system, we must first place it on sound philosophical foundation. Are we intelligently designed or simply the result of random interaction of matter?

Can we become real scientists and develop protocols to test intelligent design vs. evolution? Can we test controlling nausea and encouraging eating vs. allowing the patient to decide?

We can. To do so, we must question our belief system. We must question evolution and look at evidence for intelligent design.

Does Intelligence Exist?

I define intelligence as the ability to adapt to new situations. That ability implies a choice. If intelligence exists, it is independent of matter and controls it. If intelligence were the result of matter, there would be no choice. The physical and chemical composition of our brains would determine what we think.

The problem is one of cause and effect. An effect cannot cause itself. If Cause A causes Effect B, Effect B cannot cause itself.

We are confronted with two possibilities: 1) Intelligence existed prior to creation of the universe, intelligent design. Or, 2) Intelligence is the result of the interaction of energy/matter, evolution.

Some will claim that I have presented a false dilemma. In other words, they will claim that there exists more than those two choices. There is no merit to their claim unless they can provide the overlooked choice.

Next some will argue that the first possibility is essentially an argument for the existence of God, a claim that, it is said, cannot be falsified and is therefore unscientific using the reasoning of Popper. I reply with the words of Sir Arthur Conan Doyle "... when you have eliminated the impossible, whatever remains, however improbable, must be the truth?"[10]

By falsifying the second premise, the first, however distasteful to evolutionists, must be accepted as truth until the third possibility is presented. So I will start with the process of falsifying the second premise: Intelligence is the result of the interaction of energy/matter.

If intelligence is the result of the interaction of energy/matter, then we live a determined life. Even our thoughts were determined at the time of the big bang.

Newton's three laws of motion are the basis of classical physics. Inertia, the first law, states that a particle remains at rest or remains at a constant velocity unless acted upon by an outside force. Force equals mass times acceleration is the second law. For every action there is an equal and opposite reaction is the third law. Although the laws have formed the basis of physics, they have also posed a philosophical problem of determinism.

Imagine a giant billiard table. The balls represent the particles of matter of the Universe. If a physicist knew the position of the balls, and the velocity of the cue ball, the physicist could predict the velocity of every other ball. In the case of the Universe, the physicist could predict the future. I first encountered this philosophical problem in John Gribbin's book, explaining quantum mechanics.[11]

When we couple the above analogy with the idea that our thoughts are a result of the arrangement of the particles of our bodies, we are left with the conclusion that even our thoughts were predetermined at the time of the big bang. If we have free will and can control our thoughts and actions, then our experience goes beyond Newtonian physics. Our intelligence has to come from a source outside the universe of energy/matter.

If something changes due to outside forces, like one billiard ball being struck by another there is no such thing as an ability to adapt. What appears to be adaptation is merely the result of the interaction of forces. However, if we have an ability to adapt, if we are intelligent, the second premise is falsified. Perhaps an experiment can help answer the question.

The Intelligence, Mind, Body Experiment

I now present an experiment. Sit comfortably and raise your right hand above your head. Look at your hand. Then place your hands in your lap. Next, close your eyes and spend 30 seconds visualizing your right hand as you just did. I conducted this experiment at a seminar. In a class of over 40 people, no hand was raised during the visualization. In addition, most people found their minds drifting away from the task. Suddenly they would catch themselves thinking about something other than their right hand. When they became aware of their thoughts, they brought their minds back to the task and began again.

If our thoughts were the result of the interaction of energy/matter, then the constant bombardment of our bodies with external electromagnetic forces might account for the wandering of our minds. However, how do we explain that part of us which is aware? How do we explain that we can recognize our wandering mind and bring it back to task? How do we explain that some part of us has control over energy/matter? How do we explain that we can raise our hand intentionally without visualization?

We can either state that our awareness is outside the space/time–energy/matter realm, or we can claim that it is all illusion. If we claim that the observation of an ability to control our minds and actions is illusion, there is no point to science. Cause and effect either do not exist or we have no control.

My experience is that I am composed of intelligence that is aware of my mind and body. My intelligence was aware of my thoughts and could control them. My intelligence can control my body. The second premise is falsified. Intelligence, the ability to adapt, and free will exist and cannot be the result of the interaction of energy/matter.

Can Placebo Effect Be Explained by Evolution?

As stated previously, many people in evolution-based medicine are enamored with the mechanistic theory that intelligence is the result of the interaction of energy/matter. They also proudly point to the double blind placebo controlled clinical trial as the epitome of science.

Evolutionists are confronted with an inconsistency. If my thoughts are the result of the configuration of energy/matter of my body, then there can be no placebo effect. My thinking can only change as the result of a change in my anatomy/physiology.

Boyd and Sheldon stated that the power of placebos should not be underestimated. It was their opinion that the relief obtained was due to the "faith, confidence and trust the patient has in his caretakers."[12]

The idea that faith, confidence and trust can affect a person's well being and alter the course of disease is the basis of the so-called placebo effect. Implicit in the idea is that intelligence or mind controls matter and not the other way around.

Some may like to argue co-dependency and state that the brain is necessary to express a thought. I will agree. However, the force behind the thought is as separate from the brain as the radio signal is separate from the radio. Of course a radio is necessary to express the signal; however, the signal exists independently of the radio. Intelligence exists independently of the brain. Let's take a closer look at placebos.

If I take a sugar pill and I recover from a disease, it is said to be the result of the placebo effect and not due to the sugar pill. However, if my thoughts are the result of the interaction of energy/matter in my body, then the thought that I would get well had to have come from the change in energy/matter resulting from the sugar pill, a change in my brain. If it had any effect at all, it had to be a treatment effect. It actually made a change.

Similarly, it would be difficult to say that any medication had any effect accept that it might change energy/matter and make me believe that I would get well. Perhaps the only effect of any medication is what might have previously been misunderstood as the placebo effect.

I first recognized that fact when I was presented with a clinical trial showing that chiropractic care for headaches was no more effective than placebo.[13] The placebo used was low power laser light. However, even the placebo group did better than the control group, which was the standard treatment of analgesics. To point out the obvious, the placebo out performed the previous method of treatment. Supposedly the previous medical treatment had been proven effective against a placebo. The question then came to me, what if we pit two placebos against each other? If one placebo out performed the other, could we claim one is an effective treatment?

Those who insist that intelligence is the result of the interaction of energy/matter must give up the idea of placebo effects and come to the reality that every interaction of energy/matter has the potential of being a treatment. Therefore, they must evaluate one treatment against another and give up the term placebo. Research using a no-treatment control compared to medical treatment compared to chiropractic would be valid. Researchers claiming that sugar pills are only an appropriate placebo for medicine and not chiropractic may be attempting to substitute a more effective treatment (laser light) for comparison to chiropractic while keeping their less effective treatment (sugar pills) for comparison to medicine. That is good marketing, not good science.

However, the point is that those who believe that intelligence is the result of the evolution of energy/matter fail to realize that their belief in intelligence is deeply imbedded in their concepts of reality. The idea of placebo effect is just one example of the recognition that intelligence controls matter.

Some may argue that recognition of intelligence does not alter our behavior. We still must research the physical world. However, it does change how we approach patients and how we conduct research. It begins with the understanding of adaptation.

Health Is About Adaptation

Health is more than lack of disease. Health is optimal function. Optimal means the best choice for the circumstances at hand.

If something has the ability to adapt it possesses intelligence and is said to be intelligent. Adapt means to change to fit a new situation, a new condition, or changing environment. If something changes itself or something else for the benefit of itself, it has adapted, the change is called adaptation and the something is intelligent. If something changes due to forces external to itself, the changes may be said to be an adaptation, however the changes do not indicate any intelligence inherent in the something.

For example, if I make a coat to protect myself from a cold winter, I may be said to be intelligent. I created an adaptation, the coat. The material was adapted to become a coat and is therefore an adaptation. The coat has no intelligence. The coat did not change itself.

The example of the coat seems pretty clear. Who would argue that a coat has any intelligence? However, if our thoughts are controlled by the interaction of energy/matter, then we have no intelligence. What we consider to be adaptations are merely the result of external forces. We are no more in control of our lives and our destinies than the material was in control of itself to become a coat.

Creating adaptation requires the ability to accurately analyze a situation and reason a solution. The success of the solution is determined by the outcome of the adaptation. If an organism changes and the change results in longer life or survival of the species, it is considered a successful adaptation and the organism is deemed to be more intelligent than the one which created an unsuccessful adaptation.

Life has the ability to adapt and is therefore intelligent. Since we are born with life, we consider that intelligence to be innate, thus the name chiropractors use – innate intelligence.

How Is Intelligence Interrupted?

One of the questions we must answer, if we adopt intelligent design, is that one: How is intelligence interrupted? We must also ask: Is the body acting with purpose or is it out of control? When should we intervene? The patient with nausea and diarrhea mentioned previously is a good example. To some extent the process is natural. If the body is out of control, the person could die from dehydration. How do we determine what is wrong and when to assist?

We can state that all adaptation is the result of innate intelligence for without life all function ceases. This is a key point in the difference between medicine and chiropractic. Chiropractic is based on the premise that innate intelligence adapts the body to its environment. Successful adaptation is health. Unsuccessful adaptation results in death. Any interference to the adaptation process is dis-ease. Although every cell has its own innate intelligence, as organisms become more complex, the nervous system is used as the primary means of controlling and coordinating adaptation.

Some will argue that the function of the nervous system is well known and that there is no such controlling and coordinating effect. They will point to the nerve action potential and the movement of muscles and claim that the process is quite well understood. However, when asked to explain the research on salamanders reported by orthopedist Dr. Robert Becker they become stymied.

The salamander has the ability to re-grow a limb. Becker cited research that showed that if a nerve was routed to a different area of the salamander's body, an extra limb would grow. The extra limb that formed depended on the area of the body. If the sciatic nerve was transplanted near a foreleg, an extra foreleg grew. If the nerve was transplanted near a hind leg, an extra hind leg grew. This seems to indicate that the nervous system assists in controlling the expression of genes. Becker's book for laymen is not the only work to cite such examples. [14]

Williams and Warwick cite research showing that the nervous system has a profound effect on the establishment of the type of muscle, which is formed. They wrote that if a nerve does not connect with a muscle, both the nerve and the muscle degenerate. If a nerve to red muscle is connected to white muscle, during the course of development, the muscle changes its structure and properties to red muscle. Furthermore, the change appears to be due to the firing frequency of the nerve and not due to release of a chemical.[15]

If transplantation of nerves alters the type of tissue which forms, it seems obvious that interference to nerve function would not only alter the ability of an organism to control and coordinate multiple body functions, interference might also result in altered tissues such as cancer. That is a key understanding and the root of most disagreements between chiropractors and medical doctors. Chiropractors claim that disease is not an entity. Disease is failure to properly adapt. Syphilis is a good example.

Disease Is Not an Entity

Disease is not a thing. It is a condition of the body that is not normal and is characterized by certain symptoms and signs. The cause and prognosis may or may not be known.

We were taught in biology that syphilis is caused by a spirochete. If left untreated, the patient will develop tertiary syphilis. If we use the reasoning of Karl Popper as explained previously, all we need to do is find one case where the spirochete does not cause syphilis and the theory is falsified. So, we inject the spirochete into a corpse – nothing happens. The theory is as dead as the corpse.

Medical scientists will object that of course a living body is necessary. They will say that causes of diseases are not singular but the conjunction of factors. So, we take a group of living people and give them the spirochete. If left untreated, what happens? Boyd and Sheldon reported that only 25% of untreated patients developed symptoms or signs of tertiary syphilis after 25 years of follow up.[16]

It seems we find that 75% of untreated patients manage to adapt. This is far from the single isolated incident required to falsify the theory. It also shows that the chiropractic premise of disease as altered function, failure to adapt, is correct. Although the spirochete was present, the tertiary symptoms of the disease were not. The body did adapt in 75% of cases.

Is syphilis an isolated example? No. The fallacies of disease causation in medicine are so rampant that searching for a single falsifying event is not even considered. Instead, disease causation is reported statistically and one group is said to be at higher risk than another group. Using risk analysis is how new diseases are created.

Creating New Diseases

One night I was the speaker at a local discussion group. I presented the following idea. "In chiropractic college, I was taught a test that correlates with stroke and heart disease. Of those who perform very poorly on the test, 98.6% will not have strokes. Of those who perform very well on the test 99.9% will not have strokes. We want to go out to the public and screen everyone to get them in for treatment. Should we do it?"

The first question I got was, "Who would pay for it?"

"The insurance companies pay for everything."

Somebody finally said that to go from 98.6% to 99.9% health rate just wasn't worth it. I then told them the test was blood pressure.

The Lancet published a paper in 1990 on the relationships between blood pressure, stroke and coronary heart disease.[17] Of the 7198 people in the highest risk group (Diastolic Blood Pressure over 110 mm Hg) 100 had strokes. Of the 30119 in the lowest risk group (Diastolic Blood Pressure under 69 mm Hg) 28 had strokes.

By my analysis, 98.6% of those in the highest risk group managed to adapt to their hypertension and not have a stroke. In the lowest risk group, less adaptation was required and 99.9% adapted. The theory of stroke being caused by hypertension is clearly fallacious. The chiropractic question is not: Can we reduce hypertension? The questions are: Can we improve adaptation? Can we find the factor that caused 1.4% of those at highest risk to fail to adapt?

What about heart disease? 4.5% of those in the highest risk group had coronary heart disease. The rate for the lowest risk group dropped to .64%.

Many times we hear about our relative risk. For example, your risk of stroke is 15 times (1.4 divided by .09) greater if you have high blood pressure. Your risk of coronary heart disease is 7 times greater if you have high blood pressure. Sounds pretty convincing doesn't it?

How much greater is your risk of being healthy? If 95.4% of hypertensive people do not have heart disease and 99.36% of people with low blood pressure do not have heart disease, you barely improve your risk of being healthy by 1.04 times (99.36 divided by 95.4).

One night while speaking to a chiropractic group, I asked the group what percentage of middle aged patients would have a stroke if their diastolic blood pressure was over 110 for a ten year period. I was surprised that a common answer was 80%. Even a chiropractic group, typically skeptical of medical procedures, was way off on the actual risk of stroke or heart disease, given the most negative finding. The marketing spin has been outstanding.

In defense of the medical approach of controlling hypertension, it might be argued that by lowering blood pressure, we reduce the required adaptation and lives might be saved. However, when 98.6% of people already adapt to hypertension, it seems obvious that some other factor is involved in the remaining 1.4%. To medicate 98.6% of the hypertensive public without searching for the missing factor necessary to save the 1.4% truly at risk, gives the appearance of being more concerned for pharmaceutical sales than human life.

Before we leave this topic, I want to look at how diseases are created. Hypertension is a good example. Hypertension is not a big deal. What we are really concerned about is heart disease and stroke. The Lancet study combined 9 studies covering an average of 10 years. During those 10 years, there were totals of 449 strokes and 2190 heart events among those with diastolic blood pressures of 90 mm Hg or higher. That is an average of about 264 patients per year. The total requiring medication would have been 119,594 every year. Hypertension is now a new disease, which must be treated to prevent strokes and heart disease. It just created 116,955 (119,594 total hypertensive patients minus 2,639 patients who developed stroke or heart events) new patients who will not have either strokes or heart disease. It is all statistical nonsense. Remember that the number is not the number of patients treated nationwide, just the number from the nine studies.

Is it possible that those who have stroke or heart disease are failing to adapt due to a problem with their spines? A small study showed that hypertensive patients who had misalignment of the upper neck improved dramatically after correction.[18] The improvement was equal to two drugs combined. It would be interesting to determine if that is the missing link in the 1.4% of people who fail to adapt to their hypertension.

If we lower blood pressure, do we actually reduce the risk of heart disease and stroke? I don't know. I do know that some advertisements for drugs to lower cholesterol admit to no evidence that the risk of stroke will go down, even if the cholesterol level improves. We spend a lot of money on lowering cholesterol, is it worth it?

What about pap smears? What about mammograms? What about cholesterol screening? Is it real or is it nonsense? Who can you trust?

You probably cannot trust your doctor.

Your Doctor Is Probably Not a Statistician

Doctors love to throw around probabilities but few really understand the numbers. Most of the time, they are simply reporting some fact they read in a journal.

One doctor wrote to me that all medical treatments are proven to be 95% effective. The doctor had confused effectiveness with confidence interval. For example, a treatment might be 40% effective. Due to study design we are never 100% sure that it is 40% effective. Based on statistical analysis the result might be reported as 40% with a 95% confidence interval of 35-45%. In other words, we are 95% confident that the treatment is effective somewhere between 35-45% of the time.

Does 40% treatment effectiveness seem low to you? Me too. However, when I pull the studies that is often the result I find.

For example, what about vaccines? We are told every year to get the flu shot so that we are protected. Just how protected are we? Are we protected like a football player in full pads ready to go on the field? Or, are we completely naked and the flu shot is like handing us a helmet, right before we enter the game?

The most honest studies compare the rates of upper respiratory illness between the vaccinated group and the unvaccinated group. One well done study showed that the vaccine was 25% effective in reducing upper respiratory illness; 45% effective in reducing days of sick leave, and 44% effective in reducing visits to physicians' offices.[19] Granted, you are protected, but is that what you expected?

Perhaps you better take care of yourself. Reliance on vaccines is obviously not the key to health.

How about preventive medicine? That is getting a lot of publicity. Does it work?

Preventive Medicine - An Oxymoron

Medicine means to treat. It seems obvious to me that a disease cannot be treated and prevented simultaneously. Preventive medicine is an attempt to find diseases and treat them before they become worse. It is hardly the same as keeping you healthy.

Proponents of single payer health care often say that doctors will catch more problems earlier and we will be healthier as a result. Is that true?

In an attempt to prove the effectiveness of an intervention program, veterans discharged from Veterans Affairs hospitals were divided into control and intervention groups. They were followed for six months. The intervention group was given intensive primary care. The result was increased not decreased hospital readmission. [20]

Why are we surprised? If medical care is really the third leading cause of death in America, shouldn't we expect more care to result in more death and disability?

How Should We Evaluate a Health Care Service?

Although I advocate regular checkups for my patients, the vast majority of patients need less care over time. That should be the criteria for evaluating a health care service. If you are becoming healthier, you should need less of the service.

What procedures in evolution-based medicine are really health care services? I'll give you antibiotics, if after a brief course the patient is better and no longer needs them. I'll give you surgery, if after the surgery the patient no longer needs intervention.

Prescribing blood pressure medication for the rest of your life is not making you healthy. Prescribing cholesterol medication for the rest of your life is not making you healthy. Prescribing aspirin to prevent stroke or heart disease is not making you healthy.

Health does not come from the environment. Health does not come from a bottle of pills. It doesn't matter if the pills are aspirin or vitamin C. Health comes from intelligence.

Conclusions

Intelligence, the ability to adapt, cannot evolve from the random interaction of matter. We need to change our research endeavors to study adaptation.

Health is caused by intelligence. Intelligence adapts the body to the environment for success. Intelligence can also be used to adapt the environment.

Statistical analysis of relative risk, correlating variables to illness, is creating diseases with escalating costs of treatment. Those treatments may provide little, if any, benefit and may actually cause more problems due to side effects of treatment. Hypertension is one example. We must look at the actual base rates of correlation rather than relative risk.

Disease is not a thing. Disease is a condition of the body. Studying the body from the standpoint of intelligent design, allowing the body to heal, may be more productive than attempting to control the body externally.

We must be careful when crafting legislation that we do not further consolidate the power of evolution-based medicine. Research may show that there are more effective and less expensive alternatives.

Finally, we all want the best health care in the world when we are sick or have been involved in a traumatic event. Evolution-based medicine has created amazing treatments for emergency care. However, the philosophy is faulty. In order to help our population be as healthy as possible, we must correct our philosophy. We must study intelligence, mind, and body. We must wrest our health care system from the drug and insurance industries.

Health is one of our natural rights. It should be protected. Mandatory medical procedures may do more harm than good. Science may provide the answers, if the right questions are asked. We must break our programming. We must allow intelligence to be our guide.

Bibliography

1. Starfield, Barbara, America's Healthcare System is the Third Leading Cause of Death. http://www.health-care-reform.net/causedeath.htm accessed 07/10/09

2. Hawking SH. A Brief History Of Time. New York (NY): Bantam Books; 1988; pg. 10.

3. Webster's New Collegiate Dictionary, Springfield: G. & C. Merriam Company; 1974. Allopathy; p. 31.

4. Webster's New Collegiate Dictionary, Springfield: G. & C. Merriam Company; 1974. Chiropractic; p. 195.

5. Webster's New Collegiate Dictionary, Springfield: G. & C. Merriam Company; 1974. Homeopathy; p. 547.

6. Webster's New Collegiate Dictionary, Springfield: G. & C. Merriam Company; 1974. Naturopathy; p. 766.

7. Beck, AH. The Flexner Report and the Standardization of American Medical Education. JAMA. 2004:291(17):2139-2140. http://jama.ama-assn.org/cgi/reprint/291/17/2139 accessed 06/27/09

8. Linder, Douglas O. State v. John Scopes ("The Monkey Trial").University of Missouri-Kansas City. http://www.law.umkc.edu/faculty/projects/Ftrials/scopes/evolut.htm accessed 07/10/09

9. Carey, John. "Medical Guesswork." BusinessWeek. 29 May 2006 http://www.businessweek.com/magazine/content/06_22/b3986001.htm accessed 07/10/09.

10. Arthur Conan Doyle, Sr Quotes. ThinkExist.com accessed 07/23/09

http://thinkexist.com/quotation/once_you_eliminate_the _impossible-whatever/220272.html

11. Gribbin J. In Search Of Schrodinger's Cat: Quantum Physics and Reality. New York (NY): Bantam Books; 1984; pg. 9.

12. Boyd W, Sheldon H. Introduction to the Study of Disease. Philadelphia (PA): Lea & Febiger; 1980; pg. 57.

13. Bove G, Nilsson N. Spinal Manipulation in the Treatment of Episodic Tension-Type Headache. JAMA. 1998; 280: pgs 1576-1579.

14. Becker R, Sheldon G. The Body Electric: Electromagnetism and the Foundation of Life. New York (NY): William Morrow; 1985; pgs. 55,56.

15. Williams PL, Warwick R. Gray's Anatomy 36th Edition. London: W.B.Saunders Company; 1980; pg. 862.

16. Boyd W, Sheldon H. Indroduction to the Study of Disease. Philadelphia (PA): Lea & Febiger; 1980; pg. 626.

17. MacMahon S, Peto R, Cutler J, Collins R, Sorlie P, Neaton J, Abbott R, Godwin J, Dyer A, Stamler J. Epidemiology. Blood pressure, stroke, and coronary heart disease. The Lancet 1990; Vol 335; pg. 765-774.

18. Journal of Human Hypertension (2007) 21, 347–352. doi:10.1038/sj.jhh.1002133; published online 2 March 2007 http://www.nature.com/jhh/journal/v21/n5/abs/1002133a.ht ml   accessed 07/10/09

19. Nichol KL, Lind, A, Margolis KL, Murdoch M, McFadden R, Hauge M, Magnan s, Drake M. The Effectiveness of Vaccination Against Influenza In Healthy, Working Adults. The New England Journal of Medicine

(1995); Volume 333; Number 14; pgs 889-893.
20. Weinberger M, Oddone EZ, Henderson WG. Does Increased Access to Primary Care Reduce Hospital Readmissions? The New England Journal of Medicine (1996); Volume 334; Number 22; pgs 1441-1446.

About the Author

Dr. Affolter has been a practicing chiropractor since 1985. He graduated from Palmer College of Chiropractic in 1984. In addition to his clinical doctorate degree in chiropractic, he completed the pre-med requirements at the University of Kansas, receiving a B.A. degree in chemistry in 1977. He went on to receive a M.B.A. degree from the University of Kansas in 1978.

His articles and thoughts have been published in *Dynamic Chiropractic*, *Chiropractic and Osteopathy*, and *Journal of Vertebral Subluxation Research*. He was invited to present papers at the International Research and Philosophy Symposium (2005 and 2006) and ICA Conference on Philosophical Standards (2004 and 2005).

He resides with his wife in Bellingham, Washington.

Breinigsville, PA USA
22 October 2010
247877BV00003B/1/P